THIS ONE'S
FOR MY MUM
AND DAD

Piper

Oscar

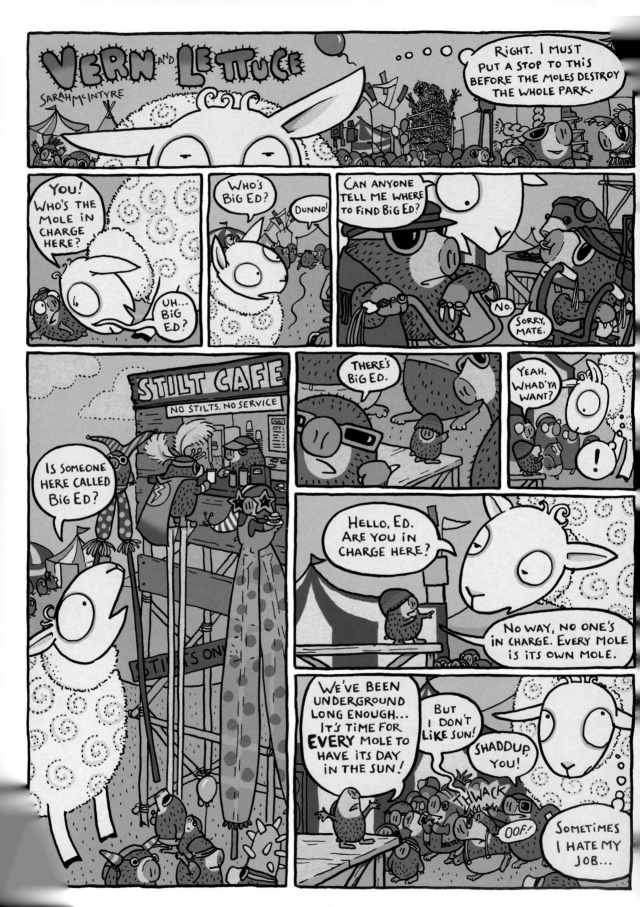

LETTUCE AND VERN'S POP AT FAME

24

VERN AND LETTUCE

SARAH McINTYRE

I DON'T THINK WE SHOULD'VE LET GERARD TALK US INTO WEARING OUR NEW CLOTHES TO HIS PARTY.

YEAH, MY DRESS KEEPS HITCHING UP.

HE'S INVITED A LOT OF POSH GUESTS...

HITCH ADJUST ADJUST

HELLO, DAHLING.

HOLY CABBAGE! THERE'S RICKY RENARD FROM 'BARNYARD TALENT'!!

VERN, WE SO HAVE TO TALK TO HIM!

WHY, HELLO, LITTLE RABBIT. AND WHAT'S YOUR NAME?

C'MON, LETTUCE, SAY SOMETHING SOPHISTICATED...

...

SORRY, MY FRIEND'S A LITTLE STAR-STRUCK.

OUCH!

!

NO, MY TAIL'S CAUGHT IN MY ZIP! OWWW!!!

VERN! I CAN'T BELIEVE I MADE SUCH AN IDIOT OF MYSELF!

AW, IT WASN'T THAT BAD!

QUICK, LETTUCE! TO THE TOILETS FOR A MOMENT OF SHAME.

(MOMENT OF SHAME)

AAA'AAAA NOOO eee URGHAOWW

WHEW, THANKS FOR THAT.

34

VERN AND LETTUCE

Sarah McIntyre

WE CAN'T GO BACK INTO GERARD'S PARTY LIKE THIS!

OUR NEW CLOTHES ARE A MESS.

LET'S CREEP BACK TO OUR ROOMS AND WE CAN CHANGE.

DO WE GO BACK IN OUR MESSED-UP CLOTHES OR TAKE THEM OFF FIRST?

OH! WE CAN'T GO THROUGH THE PARTY NAKED!

BUT VERN, YOU HARDLY EVER WEAR CLOTHES.

OH, YEAH.

GET A GRIP, WE'RE ANIMALS. AND NO ONE WILL SEE US IF WE RUN FAST.

ONE, TWO, THREE...

WHEEEEE!

OH, MY! STREAKERS!

SHOCKING!

DID SOMEONE JUST SEE TWO NAKED ANIMALS RUN BY?

WHAT'S HAPPENING? ROGER, WILL YOU INVESTIGATE?

OF COURSE, SIR.

DON'T LOOK NOW, LETTUCE, BUT YOU HAVE A BEAR BEHIND!

VERN AND LETTUCE

SARAH MCINTYRE

OOH, MOLES, WHERE **ARE** WE?

HERE WE ARE, AT A GHOST STATION!

THERE USED TO BE TRAINS HERE. BUT NOW HARDLY ANYONE KNOWS THIS PLACE.

NO EXIT

EXCEPT FOR THE GHOSTS, OF COURSE.

HUH?

AARGH!

DARN YOU, BRANDO! WE THOUGHT FOR A SECOND THAT SHEEP WAS SOMEONE ELSE!

YEAH, I ALMOST DIED OF FRIGHT!

HEY, CHILL OUT, YOU'RE ALREADY DEAD.

AARGH!

TIMID BUNCH, AREN'T THEY?!

EXIT

GRANDAD!

OH, DEAR, IT'S THAT SHEEP GHOST AGAIN!

WHAP WHAP

HE WON'T GIVE THOSE LITTLE CRITTERS ANY PEACE.

OH, NO! AM I ALSO DOOMED TO SPEND AN ETERNITY CHASING DEAD MOLES?

NAH, THAT GUY WAS JUST TOTALLY OBSESSED.

HERE THEY COME AGAIN!

REMIND ME TO GET ANOTHER HOBBY WHEN WE GET HOME, OK, LETTUCE?